Sydney Harris grew up in Santa Claus, Indiana. Her zealous personality makes her a stranger to no one, and she is passionate about making everyone around her feel loved. At the University of Southern Indiana, Sydney earned her Bachelor's of Social Work, and she has earned her Master's of Education in Mental Health Practices in Schools from the University of Missouri. Some Bodies Need a Little Help, her debut book, cultivates her passion for inclusion and acceptance. "Inclusivity matters. Especially amongst children."

Some Bodies Need a Little Help

S. F. Harris

Austin Macauley Publishers™
LONDON • CAMBRIDGE • NEW YORK • SHARJAH

Ordering Information

Quantity sales: Special discounts are available on quantity purchases by corporations, associations, and others. For details, contact the publisher at the address below.

Publisher's Cataloging-in-Publication data

Harris, S. F.

Some Bodies Need a Little Help

ISBN 9781685628321 (Paperback)

ISBN 9781685628338 (Hardback)

ISBN 9781685628345 (ePub e-book)

Library of Congress Control Number: 2023906996

www.austinmacauley.com/us

First Published 2023

Austin Macauley Publishers LLC

40 Wall Street, 33rd Floor, Suite 3302

New York, NY 10005

USA

mail-usa@austinmacauley.com

+1 (646) 5125767

This book is dedicated to everyone that has ever believed in me. Thank you.

I would like to give special thanks to Sarah Doan and ShiAne Gibson for their dedication and commitment to the success of their friends.

Everybody has
a good body,
Each one
different in
their own way.

6

Some bodies
need a little
help,
To move, to
see, to play.

Some bodies
need a chair to
move,
Even braces,
walkers, canes.

Some bodies
need prosthetic
limbs,
To travel or jam
on the drums.

All bodies are
built different,
Mobility isn't
the same for
everyone.

Some bodies need a little help,
If their hearing is impaired.

Some bodies have aids to help them hear,
Or they talk by using sign.

Some bodies may need to use both,
And this is totally fine!

Some bodies need
a little help,
If they are visually
impaired or blind.

Some bodies
read by using
Braille,
Or need
glasses custom
designed.

Some bodies
navigate using
canes,
And some
have guide
dogs specially
trained.

Some bodies need a little help,

To eat throughout the day.

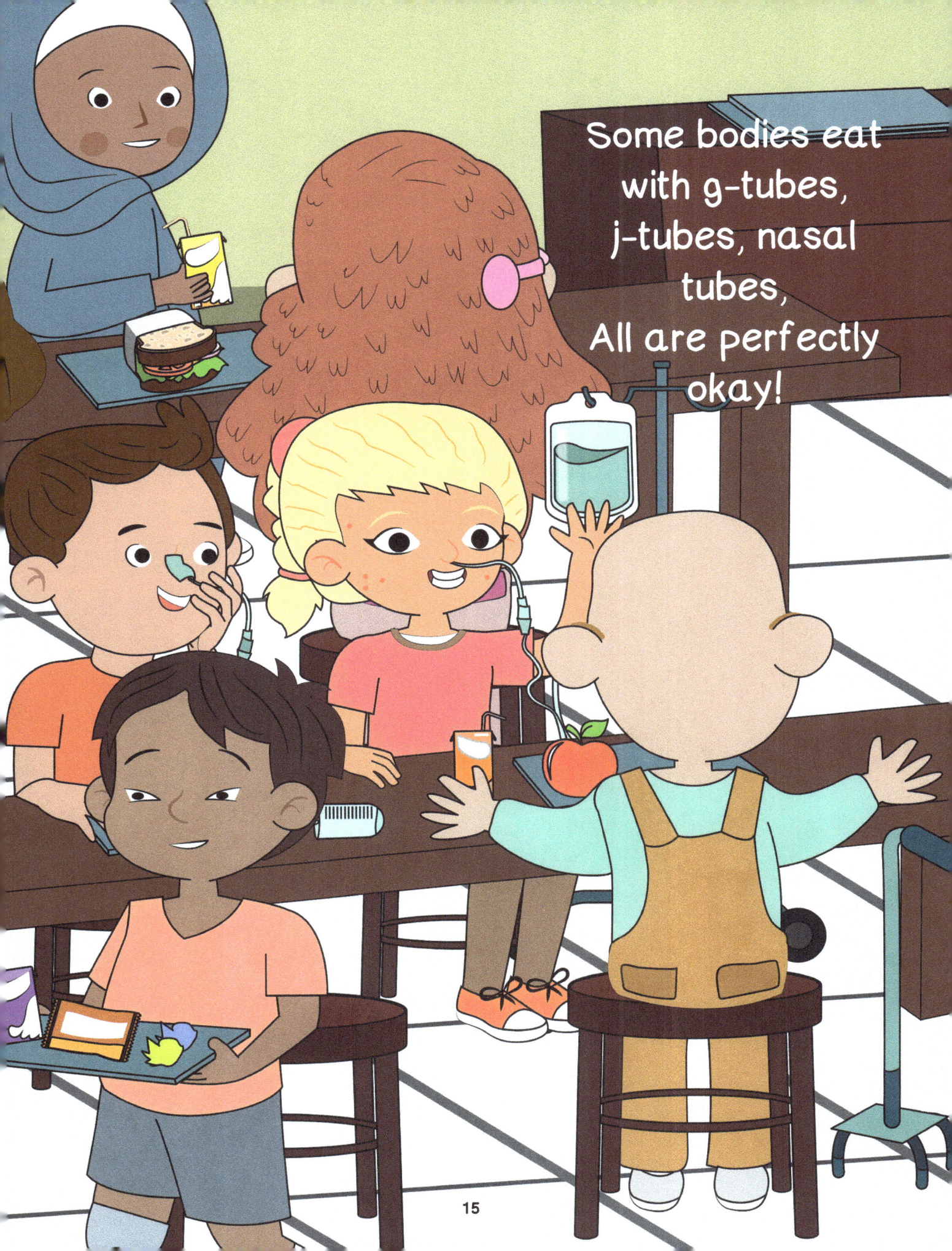

Some bodies eat
with g-tubes,
j-tubes, nasal
tubes,
All are perfectly
okay!

15

Some bodies
need a little help,
When going to the
bathroom.

Some bodies need to use a bag,
But please, it's not a costume.

Some bodies
need a little help,
So they wear
special gear.

Some bodies wear
helmets, need extra
air,
These keep some
bodies safe, so
please, try not to
stare.

Some bodies need
a little help,
Whether they are
tall or short.

So,
everybody,
love your
body,
It's okay
to need
support!

21

www.ingramcontent.com/pod-product-compliance
Lightning Source LLC
Chambersburg PA
CBHW042146240326
41723CB00013B/609